INCREDIBLE 3D STEREOGRAMS

‹EYE›
TRICKS

INCREDIBLE 3D STEREOGRAMS
‹EYE›
TRICKS

Gary W. Priester and Gene Levine

Capella

Gary W. Priester lives in Placitas, New Mexico USA and can be contacted via e-mail at gary@gwpriester.com. To see additional works created by Gary, please visit http://www.gwpriester.com.

Gene Levine lives in Los Angeles, California USA and can be contacted via e-mail at gene_levine@colorstereo.com. To see additional works created by Gene, please visit http://www.colorstereo.com.

This book was created in association with eyetricks.com. For more information visit http://www.eyetricks.com.

This edition published in 2007 by Arcturus Publishing Limited
26/27 Bickels Yard, 151–153 Bermondsey Street,
London SE1 3HA

ISBN: 978-1-84193-268-2

Printed in Singapore

Author accreditation
Images on pages 8-26, 28-59, 110, 140-143, 165-169, 172-179, 182-187, 189-207 were designed and created by Gene Levine. Images on pages 27, 60-109, 111-139, 144-164, 170-171, 180-181 and 188 are the design and creation of Gary W. Priester.

Contents

How to view stereograms

This is intended as a guide for viewers who have never seen stereogram 3D effects, and for those viewers who are a bit rusty. Please don't be discouraged if you can't visualize the effects right away. After all, what you are doing is overcoming a lifetime habit of viewing everything with 'normal' stereovision: that which gives us a sense of depth in our everyday viewing of the world.

First, let's try using a physical aid. After that are some practices for viewing autostereograms (stereograms that work without physical aids).

To view hidden-image and stereo-field stereograms, you cannot use normal, or cross-eyed vision (see fig. 1). Instead, you have to use parallel vision, which is what you will do automatically if you place a piece of card between your eyes when viewing the images (see fig. 2).

Unlike cross-eyed vision, there is no strain or discomfort with parallel vision. The essential key, in fact, is to relax your eyes into viewing this way.

Below is a stereo-pair image. Place the card directly in the middle of the pair, as illustrated in fig. 2. Now move your head to position the other end of the card between your eyes. Disregard focusing for now.

A stereo-pair

If the alignment is good, you should see only one image. Now relax your eyes, and slowly bring things into focus, pulling your head back. Remember, you should not think you see a 3D effect; you should know for sure. When you are sure, hold that focus and remove the card. You should now see three images: the one in the middle containing the 3D effects.

Congratulations, you are now viewing a stereogram as it should be seen!

Continue with the practices without aids, opposite. The only thing you'll need here is two eyes. Let go of the normal way you focus on something on a page. Let your eyes relax.

fig. 1 **Normal vision**   fig. 2 **Parallel vision**

Cardboard

Image   Image

Top view

Viewing practice for autostereograms

Practice 1

The objective here is to let your mind process these two objects until they appear as three. Let your eyes relax, and move your head forward or away until three zeros appear clearly.

Your primary inclination is to focus on the above two objects in the normal way. But now, look behind them; look behind the page and forget about focusing. Try this for a while until you gradually see the three zeros.

When you see a non-existent object appear between the two existing ones, you have mastered the basis of the stereopair. It is in the centre object where the 3D effect takes place. This is the crux of autostereograms.

So where does the centre image come from?

It is helpful to remember that visual perception happens in the brain, not the eyes. What we're doing here is fooling the brain. The eyes are feeding it visual information, but not in the usual manner, and so the mind gives us a middle object. And if you introduce some subtle offsets and distortions into two otherwise similar images, the mind will perceive depth even though it is not truly there.

If you view three objects as an autostereogram, you should perceive four objects. Four objects will look as if they are five, and so on.

Practice 2

And now for some 3D:

Between these two objects, another object should appear with the smaller square floating over the larger.

Practice 3

Still can't see it?

Pull back, and focus normally on the centre object of the three below. Now lean slowly forward into the page, holding that focus until it is broken or you see four objects, clearly.

Master these practices, and you should have no problem moving on to fully-fledged autostereograms.

Practice 4

view this way

view this way

© 2002 GENE LEVINE

view this way

© 2004 GENE LE

view this way

Blossom Waves

view this way

view this way

© 2004

view this way

view this way

© 2004 GENE LEVINE

Egyptian Shadows

view this way

view this way

Stereocycle

view this way

view this way

view this way

view this way

© 2004 GENE LEVINE

© 1998 GENE LEVINE

view this way

view this way

view this way

© 2001 GENE LEVINE

Point Burst

view this way

view this way

view this way

view this way

view this way

© 2003 GENE LEVINE

view this way

Butterfly Pillows

view this way

view this way

Colour Sieve

view this way

© 2003 GENE LEVINE

view this way

view this way

© 2003 GENE LEVINE

view this way

view this way

© 2008 GENE LEVINE

view this way

view this way

© 2004 GENE LEVINE

view this way

© 2003 GENE LEVINE

view this way

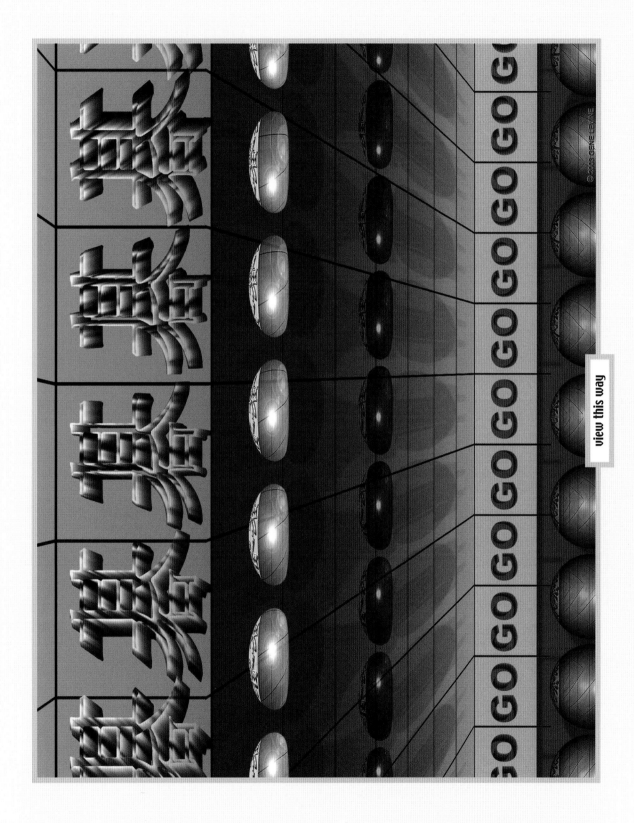

view this way

©2003 GENE LEVINE

Fireworks

view this way

44

view this way

Footprints

view this way

© 2004 GENE LEVINE

view this way

Gold Eye Sky

view this way

view this way

view this way

© 2003 GENE LEVINE

view this way

© 2002 GENE LEVINE

view this way

© 2004 GENE LEVINE

view this way

© 200_ GENE LEVINE

view this way

© 2003 GENE LEVINE

Heart-throb

view this way

view this way

© 2004 GENE LEV

view this way

Seahorse Herd

view this way

view this way

Box in a Box

view this way

Celtic Knot

view this way

view this way

Dice

view this way

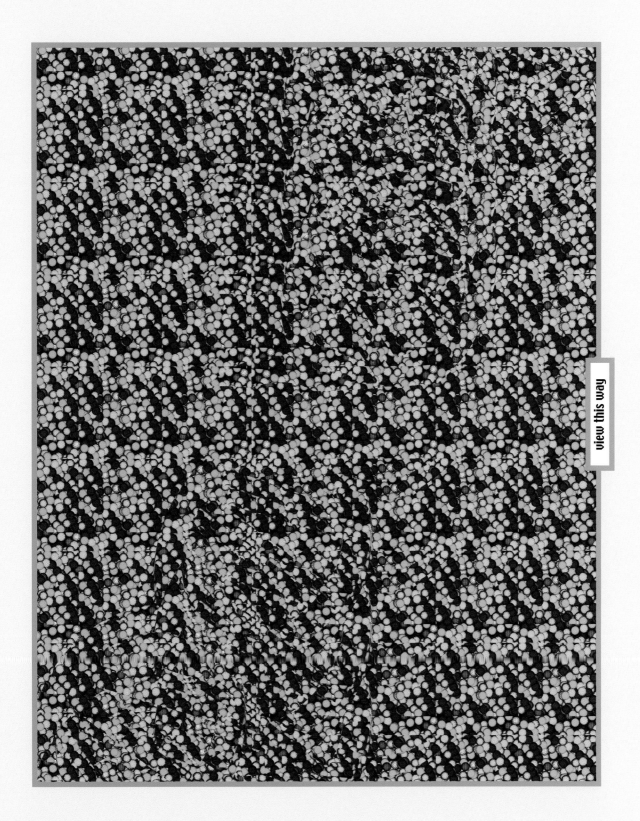

view this way

Dos Espirales

view this way

view this way

Hello

view this way

view this way

Indented Cubes

view this way

view this way

Lock & Key

view this way

view this way

view this way

view this way

view this way

view this way

view this way

Sunflower

view this way

view this way

view this way

view this way

Anasazi Petroglyphs

view this way

view this way

Cards

view this way

Circles

Cube & Hoop

view this way

view this way

view this way

view this way

Golden Medley

view this way

94

Hole in my Heart

view this way

view this way

Interlocking Stars

view this way

view this way

Officer Winkie

view this way

view this way

Pluses

view this way

102

view this way

view this way

view this way

view this way

view this way

view this way

view this way

Winter Trees

view this way

view this way

Magic Cube

view this way

112

view this way

view this way

view this way

Owl

view this way

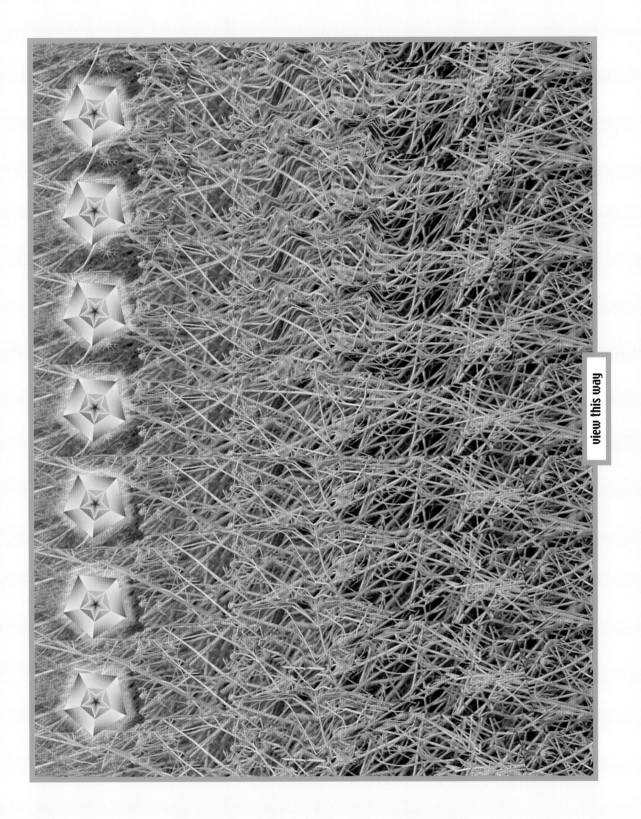

view this way

Pine Wedges

view this way

view this way

Rock Star

view this way

view this way

view this way

view this way

Susan's Basket

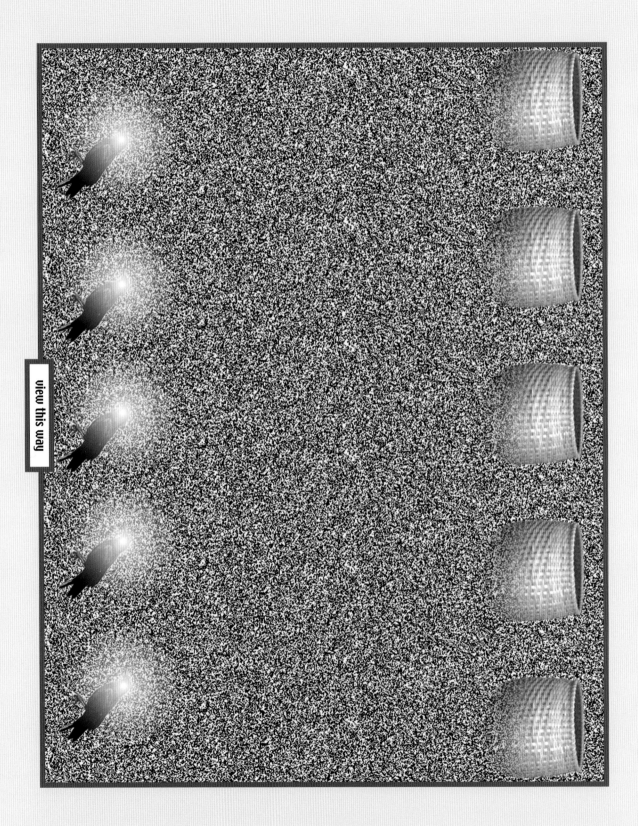

view this way

Teddy Bear

view this way

view this way

Cross Plus

view this way

view this way

Lizard Bowls

view this way

view this way

Oak Leaves

view this way

view this way

Pool Balls

view this way

view this way

©2005 GENE LEVINE

© 2003 GENE LEVINE

view this way

Organic Vacuum

view this way

view this way

view this way

view this way

view this way

view this way

view this way

view this way

view this way

Chrome Capsule

view this way

Dangerous Sea

view this way

view this way

Desert Pyramid

view this way

view this way

view this way

Interlocking Rings

view this way

view this way

Happy Face

view this way

view this way

Ivy Cube

view this way

view this way

view this way

(c) 2001 by G. Levine

view this way

Wedgwood Blue

view this way

view this way

Kaleidoscopic Spiral

view this way

view this way

view this way

view this way

(C) 1998 G Levine

view this way

view this way

Sunset on the Nile

view this way

view this way

view this way

© 2004 GENE

view this way

view this way

view this way

view this way

view this way

view this way

view this way

view this way

view this way

Floating Eyes

view this way

view this way

view this way

© 2003 GENE LEVINE

Byzantine Crystal

view this way

Rose Rows

view this way

view this way

view this way

view this way

Blue Butterfly

view this way

view this way

Butterfly Scarf

view this way

view this way

view this way

view this way

Swimming Ocean

view this way

view this way

Sunset

view this way

© 2002 GENE LEV

view this way

Revelations

page 8   Stereo Time

page 9   Aster Turf

page 10   London Disconnect

page 11   Shamrocks

page 12   Blossom Waves

page 13   Fruit Bat

page 14   Cherry Blossom

page 15   Crown Thee

page 16   Egyptian Shadows

page 17   Footsteps

Revelations

page 18   Stereocycle

page 19   Sundial

page 20   Lake View

page 21   Head Bands

page 22   Wing Wang

page 23   The Yard

page 24   King & Queen

page 25   Glad Plaid

page 26   Point Burst

page 27   Flowers with a Twist

Revelations

page 28 **Diamonds in the Rough**

page 29 **Dragonfly Sparks**

page 30 **Johnny's Garden**

page 31 **Frax Bubbles**

page 32 **Butterfly Pillows**

page 33   Cloud Funnels

page 34   Colour Sieve

page 35   Dragon Light

page 36   Molten Water

page 37   Mixed Vegetables

Revelations

page 38   Star Screen

page 39   Star Family

page 40   Man & Woman

page 41   Making Honey

page 42   Hidden Image

page 43   Go

page 44   Fireworks

page 45   Floral Twists

page 46   Footprints

page 47   Escargot

Revelations

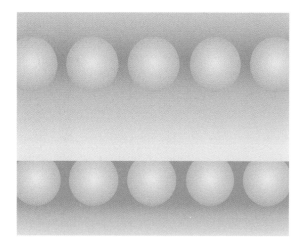

page 48 Gold Eye Sky

page 49 Goldfish

page 50 Stone Burst

page 51 The Phrenologist

page 52   Takeoff & Landing

page 53   Temple Albathor

page 54   Heart in Heart

page 55   Heart-throb

Revelations

page 56   Terraced

page 57   The Guardian

page 58   Seahorse Herd

page 59   The Stereogram Machine

page 60   Box in a Box

page 61   Butterfly

page 62   Celtic Knot

page 63   Comedy

Revelations

page 64   Dice

page 65   DNA

page 66   Dos Espirales

page 67   Double Spiral

page 68　Fantasy Nouveau

page 69　Han-nya

page 70　Hello

page 71　Hot-Air Balloon

Revelations

page 72   Indented Cubes

page 73   Inverted Spheres

page 74   Lock & Key

page 75   Mystic Shapes

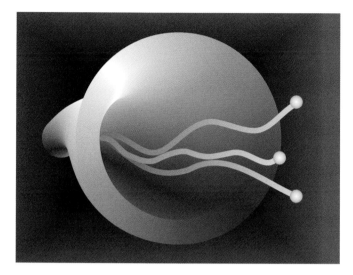

page 76   An Interesting Shape

page 77   Rings

page 78   Entanglements

page 79   Shamrock

Revelations

page 80   Star

page 81   Star of David

page 82   Sunflower

page 83   Trilogy 1

page 84   Trilogy 2

page 85   5 Rings

page 86   Anasazi Petroglyphs

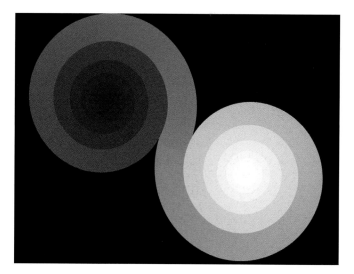

page 87   Artemisia Spirals

Revelations

page 88   Cards

page 89   Circles

page 90   Cube & Hoop

page 91   Desert Flower

page 92 Equinox

page 93 Floating Cheese Burgers

page 94 Golden Medley

page 95 Grass Cylinder

Revelations

page 96   Hole in my Heart

page 97   Hole in the Desert

page 98   Interlocking Stars

page 99   The Maze

page 100   Officer Winkie

page 101   Opposites Attract

page 102   Pluses

page 103   Pyramids – In & Out

Revelations

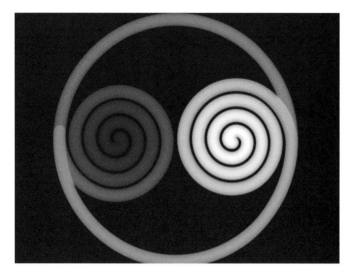

page 104   Spirals – In & Out

page 105   Square Staircase

page 106   Infinity 1

page 107   Twisting Star

page 108   Window

page 109   Words

page 110   Winter Trees

page 111   Leafy Globe

Revelations

page 112　Magic Cube

page 113　Marble Star

page 114　Mixed Messages

page 115　Mystic Tubes

page 116   Owl

page 117   Pentagon Star

page 118   Pine Wedges

page 119   Planets

Revelations

page 120 Spiral Star

page 121 Rocky Star

page 122 Snow Angel

page 123 Spiral 8

page 124   Rock Star

page 125   Split Circles

page 126   Piggy

page 127   Stereogram

Revelations

page 128   Susan's Basket

page 129   Teddy Bear

page 130   Vertigo

page 131   Windmill

page 132   Cross Plus

page 133   Celtic Knot

page 134   Lizard Bowls

page 135   Morning Glory

Revelations

page 136   Oak Leaves

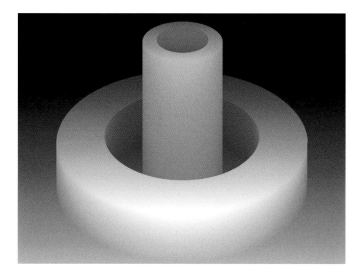

page 137   Pipe & Ring

page 138   Pool Balls

page 139   Stars & Stripes

page 140   New Mexico

page 141   Open the Door

page 142   Organic Vacuum

page 143   Orchid Hedge

Revelations

page 144   1 to 10

page 145   Abalone

page 146   Abalone Shell

page 147   Amphora

page 148　Banner

page 149　Blue Angel

page 150　Building Blocks

page 151　Celadon

Revelations

page 152   Chrome Capsule

page 153   Clover Leaf

page 154   Dangerous Sea

page 155   Deep Hole

page 156   Desert Pyramid

page 157   Enigma Circles

page 158   Eye of the Storm

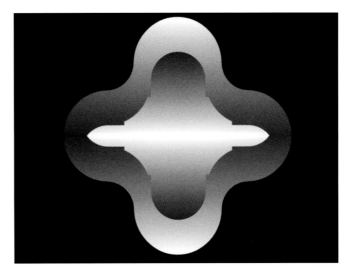

page 159   Flip Flop

Revelations

page 160   Interlocking Rings

page 161   Infinity 2

page 162   Happy Face

page 163   Infinity 3

page 164   Ivy Cube

page 165   Pound Note

page 166   Stereosaurs

page 167   Reflections of Chicago

Revelations

page 168　Wedgwood Blue

page 169　Torus Cage

page 170　Kaleidoscopic Spiral

page 171　Chrome Jungle

page 172   Granite Fu

page 173   Black Cat in a Coalmine

page 174   French Chow

page 175   Enbubbled

page 176   Sunset on the Nile

page 177   Rising Sun

page 178   Lucky Rabbit

page 179   Mesa Verde

page 180   Forest Birds

page 181   Two Hearts

page 182   Sea Palace

page 183   River Canopy

Revelations

page 184   Inspiration

page 185   Jade Riches

page 186   Lotus Garden

page 187   Koa Construction

Revelations

page 188   Floating Eyes

page 190   Byzantine Crystal

page 189   Palais du Lac

page 191   Edge of the Woods

Revelations

page 192   Rose Rows

page 193   Scorpions

page 194   Four Hundred 50 Yen

page 195   Straight as an Arrow

page 196   Blue Butterfly

page 197   Butterfly Lines

page 198   Butterfly Scarf

page 199   Holding Pattern

Revelations

page 200   Pyramid Valley

page 201   Yang Yin

page 202   Swimming Ocean

page 203   End of the Line

page 204   Sunset

page 205   Atmosphere

page 206   Uproar

page 207   Mermaid